Magic Mates

with
Stars in their Eyes

Jane West

Illustrated by
Stik

RISING STARS

Rising Stars UK Ltd.
22 Grafton Street, London W1S 4EX
www.risingstars-uk.com

The right of Jane West to be identified as the author of this work has been asserted by her in accordance with the Copyright, Design and Patents Act 1988.

Published 2008

Cover design: Button plc
Illustrator: Stik, Bill Greenhead for Illustration
Text design and typesetting: Andy Wilson
Publisher: Gill Budgell
Editor: Jane Wood

British Library Cataloguing in Publication Data.
A CIP record for this book is available from the British Library

ISBN: 979 1 84680 329 1

Printed in the UK by CPI Bookmarque, Croydon, CR0 4TD

Mixed Sources
Product group from well-managed
forests and other controlled sources
www.fsc.org Cert no. TT-COC-002227
© 1996 Forest Stewardship Council
FSC

Contents

Meet the Magic Mates

The Magic Mates are best friends –
but that doesn't mean they're all alike.

Name: *Izzie*

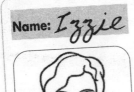

The sporty one: can climb trees,
surf and take on the boys
at their own game – and win.

Travels by: running!

Loves: trendy tracksuits, open skies
and sandy beaches.

Hates: standing still.

Name: *Meena*

The girly one: uses her mobile
for networking and planning
her social life.

Travels by: Mum's car (her personal
chauffeur).

Loves: pink and her Magic Mates.

Hates: breaking a nail.

Name: *Ginger*

The ginger one: you don't wanna mess with this feisty gal – the Kung Fu and quick quip queen!

Travels by: push-scooter.

Loves: Jackie Chan and her Magic Mate pals.

Hates: nail extensions.

Name: Jo

The clever one: uses her brains and quick wit to talk her way out of trouble. Sometimes she's a bit too quick.

Travels by: bicycle and is designing a pair of motorised rollerblades.

Loves: Jacqueline Wilson, Cathy Cassidy and Albert Einstein.

Hates: being called 'geek', 'nerd', 'swot' or 'boffin'.

Name: 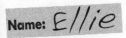 Ellie

The fashion-conscious one: can tell her Prada from her Asda and knows how to accessorise.

Travels by: limousine, of course! (But only in her dreams.)

Loves: shopping.

Hates: anything to do with getting dirty; anyone who upsets her Magic Mates.

Name: Yash

The funky punky one: the 'alternative' one of the gang who hugs trees, people and furry animals.

Travels by: skateboard.

Loves: having a good time.

Hates: bullies.

Little Voice

The school talent show has a great prize.
It's the chance to sing with the famous
pop singer Justin Timberpuddle.
Meena really wants to win.
There's just one problem.
Meena can't sing!

Ginger   This is so cool! Justin Timberpuddle is coming to our school!

Ellie   He's really cute.

Izzie   And he's a really good singer.

Meena   I think he's great! I really want to win and sing with him.

Jo   But, Meena … you can't sing!

Meena I know. What can I do?

Yash   Don't worry, Meena. We'll find a
           way to help you.

Some of the others in the class are
listening. They are really mean about
Meena wanting to sing in the talent show.

Girl 1   Meena will need all the help
           she can get!

Boy 1   When she sings it's like a frog
           with a sore throat!

Girl 2   I don't know why you are
           even trying. Everyone knows
           that Britney Lance
           is going to win.

Yash   Meena is going to sing
            in the talent show.

Ellie   Yes, she is, whatever
            nasty things you say.

Ginger   Yes. And she's going to win.

Girl 1   Ha, ha, ha! She's got more
            chance of winning the Lottery.

Boy 1   She's got more chance
            of flying to the moon.

Meena is really upset. The Magic Mates
try to make her feel better.

Meena   They're right. I've got no chance
of winning the talent show
and no chance of singing
with Justin Timberpuddle.

Yash   We're not giving up.

Ginger   We'll think of something.

Izzie   We're your friends, Meena.
We won't let you down.

Ellie   Yes! We're your Magic Mates.

Jo   I think I've got an idea!

Jo explains her idea to the Magic Mates.
They think it's a brilliant idea!
Clever Jo! This could be just the thing
to help Meena win the talent show.
But it's top secret!

Jo   Izzie and I will write the words
            for you, and Ginger and Ellie
            will find the right music for you
            to sing along to.

Ginger   Yes, I don't think Mrs Pasty would be able to play this song on the piano!

Ellie   Ha, ha, ha!
It would be very funny!

Yash   I'll help you work out some dance moves to go with it.

Ginger   Don't forget to put
some Kung Fu moves in, too!

Yash   You and your Kung Fu!
This is a talent show, not a fight!

Ginger   I wouldn't be too sure
about that. Britney Lance
has been telling everyone
she's going to win.
She doesn't
like losing.

Jo   There's a first time
for everything. And I have
a feeling that Britney Lance
isn't going to win this
talent show.

The Sound of Music

Yash is helping Meena learn some
dance moves for the talent show.
Meena is better at dancing than she
is at singing, but she's very nervous.

Meena	What if everyone laughs at me?
Yash	Why would anyone do that?
Meena	Because I'll look stupid.

Yash   No, you won't.
You'll look really good.

Meena   I hope you're right.

Yash   I am. And don't forget –
all the Magic Mates are helping.
We won't let you down.

Meena   I'm so lucky to have
such brilliant friends.
You really are Magic Mates.

The girls are using an empty classroom to practise. Then Mrs Pasty, their teacher, walks in.

Mrs Pasty What are you doing in here, girls? And what is that terrible noise?

Yash Meena is practising for the talent show.

Mrs Pasty Oh dear! Was that you singing? I thought somebody was being ill. Oh well, I'll leave you to it.

Meena   Oh no! My singing is so bad that Mrs Pasty thought somebody was being ill. This is never going to work.

Yash   It doesn't matter. Mrs Pasty doesn't like any new music. Let's concentrate on your song.

Meena   Why bother? I'll never win.

Yash   Don't give up yet, Meena. I've got another idea.

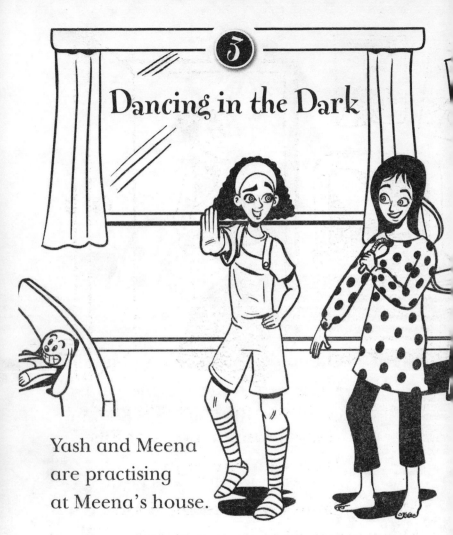

Dancing in the Dark

Yash and Meena
are practising
at Meena's house.

Meena   I think I'm getting
the hang of it now.

Yash   You're doing really well.
You look really good.

Meena Thanks, Yash. I couldn't have done it without you – or Ellie, Izzie, Ginger and Jo.

Meena's mum knocks on the door. She wonders what they're doing.

Meena's mum

Are you all right, girls? What is all that noise about?

Meena   Mum! It's not noise!
I'm practising for
the talent show!

Meena's mum

I don't know why
you can't do something nice
like Mudras hand dancing.
You're very good
at that.

Meena   Mum, it's a
talent show,
not a history
lesson!

Meena's mum

Don't be cheeky!
Lots of my friends teach
their daughters Mudras
hand dancing.

Meena　　I'm sorry, Mum. But I don't
want to do that. Yash and my
other friends have come up with
a really cool song and dance.

Yash　　Would you like to hear it,
Mrs Patel?

Meena's mum

I have already heard it
through the walls! But I will
come to your talent show.
I'm sure I will be very proud
of you. Here, have these biscuits
– I just made them.

Meena's mum goes. The girls carry on
practising.

Meena	Mum is so old fashioned.
Yash	Yes, but she makes really nice biscuits. Anyway, she said she'd come to the talent show. I think she's going to be surprised.
Meena	I just hope it's a nice surprise when she sees me sing and dance.
Yash	Oh, Meena! You'll be great! I promise!

4

Stage Coach

The school hall is full of people.
Yash looks through the curtains
on the stage. Everyone in the school
is there: all the pupils, teachers,
assistants, cooks and other helpers.
Even the caretaker, Mr Crosse, is there.
There's a reporter with a camera
from the local paper, too.
Everyone is very excited!

Yash   Wow! Everyone is here.
Even a reporter from
the local paper!

Meena   I feel sick.

Yash   Don't worry. That's just nerves.

Meena   Is Justin Timberpuddle here yet?

Yash   No, I don't think so.
But Britney Lance is here.
Have you seen
what she's wearing?
Ha, ha, ha!

Britney Lance is dressed like the fairy
on the top of a Christmas tree.
Her costume is bright pink
and she's wearing a crown
with sweets glued to it.

Yash   Er ... great costume, Britney.
What is it?

Britney   I'm the Sugar Plum Fairy,
of course. Anyone can see that!
What on earth
is Meena wearing?

Meena   I'm not wearing
anything special, just jeans,
a T-shirt, trainers
and a baseball cap.

Britney   I can see that.
Where's your costume?

Meena   This is my costume.

Britney   Well, I don't think it's very good.
You haven't made any effort,
have you?

Britney goes.
Meena is a bit upset
but Yash makes her feel better.

Yash   You'll be great, Meena.
Don't worry about Britney.

Meena   I don't care what she thinks.
I know my Magic Mates
have really helped me.
That's what matters.

Junior School Musical

A big shout goes up from the audience.
Two girls scream and one boy faints.
Justin Timberpuddle is here!

Mrs Pasty Hello, everyone, and welcome to
our talent show. We're very
lucky to have the pop singer
Justin Timberpuddle with us
to help judge our show.
Thank you, Justin!
Now, on with the show.

The first person is a little girl who sings
a song about an ugly duckling.
Everyone claps her.

The second person is a boy who sings
a song about a dog called Shep.
It is a very sad song.

Now it is Britney's turn. Meena thinks
that even with her pink, sparkly costume,
Britney is very good. She sings a song
about a fairy called Sugar Plum
and then does some ballet dancing.
Everyone claps.

Now it is Meena's turn. She can see her Magic Mates sitting in the hall. They are all smiling and clapping. Yash gives her a 'thumbs up'.

The music starts and Meena dances on to the stage. But she isn't singing! Everyone says Meena can't sing – and she can't. But she can dance. And she can rap!

Meena

This is the way
I do the Meena rap
My fingers start to move
And my feet start to tap
My body starts to sway
I hear music in my head
My heart feels light
And I forget what they said
They say I cannot sing
But it doesn't mean a thing
Because while they yap
I can rap, rap, rap.

This is the way
I do the Meena hop
My toes start to wiggle
And my feet want to bop
My body starts to sway
I hear music in my head
My heart feels light
And I forget what they said
They say I cannot dance
But it doesn't mean a thing
Because when they stop
I can hip, hap, hop.

Everyone is clapping and cheering!
Hurrah! Meena's rap is really good.
And the best bit is when
Justin Timberpuddle smiles
and blows her a kiss. Meena feels
so happy: all thanks to her best friends
in the world – her Magic Mates.

About the Author

Jane West's favourite rap poem is by a poet called Jack Ousbey. The poem is called 'Gran, Can You Rap?' and it's all about a granny who does a really good rap!

Jane West:

- lives by the beach in Cornwall
- likes taking Pip paddling in the sea
- has worked in an art gallery, a bookshop and a school.

Now she's a writer, and has had great fun writing about the Magic Mates. She hopes you liked reading about them.

Feeling Nervous

Most people feel nervous like Meena
before they go on stage. It's called 'stage fright'.
Here are some things to help you feel
less nervous if you get stage fright.

 Make sure you have practised
as much as you need to.
Practise, practise, practise!

 Close your eyes and breathe slowly,
but not too deeply.

 If you have a dry mouth, drink some water.

 Your muscles will feel tense.
Hold them tight, then relax them slowly.

 Shake your hands. It helps relax
all your muscles.

 Tell yourself: 'Yes, I can.
Yes, I will!'

You Are Not Alone!

Lots of famous actors, singers and dancers get stage fright.

Singer Rod Stewart once got stage fright when he was singing in New York.
He was so nervous that he sang the first song from behind the speakers!

When the famous actor Laurence Olivier was in a play, he had to be pushed on stage by the stage manager every night!

'The only way is to go on stage
and to hope.'

Andrea Bocelli, opera singer

'Some performers really do well
when they forget the words.
They forget the words all the time,
but they somehow have humour about it.'

Barbara Streisand, singer

'Great events make me quiet and calm;
it is only trifles that irritate my nerves.'

Queen Victoria

Karaoke Singing

Have you ever sung karaoke? Karaoke is when you sing well-known songs to a backing track of music.

'Karaoke' is a Japanese word. It means 'empty orchestra'. Do you think this is a good word for karaoke singing?

The top four karaoke songs are:

'Angels' by Robbie Williams

'I Will Survive' by Gloria Gaynor

'Suspicious Minds' by Elvis Presley

'Dancing Queen' by Abba.

Which songs would you have on your karaoke song list?

Joke Time

Girl 1	Wow! What a nice silver medal! How did you win it?
Girl 2	By singing.
Girl 1	And how did you win the gold medal?
Girl 2	By stopping!

Why do people rock from side to side when they are singing on stage?

Because it's more difficult to hit a moving target!

Quiz

1 What does the word 'karaoke' mean?

2 Suggest three things that will make you feel less nervous before you go on stage.

3 Where did singer Rod Stewart hide when he got stage fright?

4 What irritated Queen Victoria?

5 What is the most popular karaoke song?

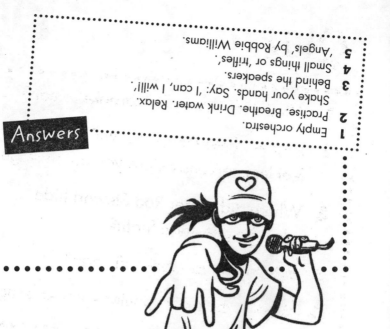

Answers

1 Empty orchestra.
2 Practise. Breathe. Drink water. Relax. Shake your hands. Say: 'I can, I will!'.
3 Behind the speakers.
4 Small things or 'trifles'.
5 'Angels', by Robbie Williams.

How did you score?

0–1 I think you've got stage fright!

2–3 Well done! You are getting over your stage fright!

4–5 You're a talent show trouper!

Magic Mates

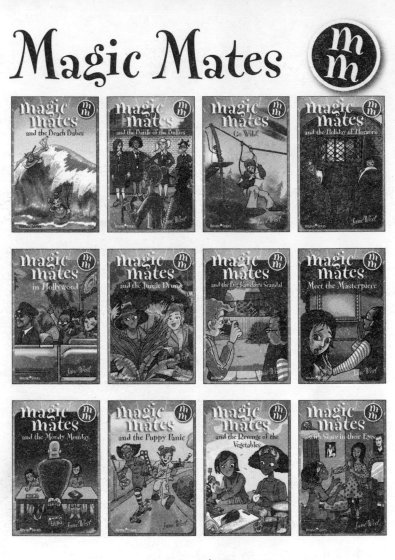

RISING ✦ STARS